In praise of **Hi, I'm Me**

"*Motivated by an inspirational and lovable little girl with a magneti̇c̶ has created Confidently Chloe. Chloe encourages readers to respon̶ with courage, charm, and assuredness. This book is a delightful wa̶y̶ ̶.̶.̶.̶veness and feelings of positive self-worth.*"

> ~ **Ariella Folman**, Early Childhood Consultant

"*...a brilliant and moving story about a little girl who embraces her differences while inspiring everyone around her. Kelly's book provides children with an important tool to be accepted and to accept others. A must-read for every classroom teacher.*"

> ~ **Sandra Holmes**, Resource Consultant

"*Kelly Vurinaris is an author who combines real-life situations in an endearing and thought-provoking story based on her daughter. This book is a must read for any educator, parent, family member or friend, who needs a teaching tool to assist people to understand that differences are what make us unique.* **Hi, I'm Me** *is truly an inspirational book about acceptance. A global story that will touch the lives of many children around the world.*"

> ~ **Pashmina P.**, International Best-Selling Author of *What is a Gupsey?* and
> *The Cappuccino Chronicles Trilogy*

"*Words are powerful. Using words in a calm, positive manner is an empowering life skill. In this book, Chloe is learning to use her words to initiate conversation and begin social interaction. Whether read one-on-one, in a small group, or in a classroom setting,* **Hi, I'm Me** *will open opportunities for gentle, sensitive discussion with children. It will also prod adults to a deeper, heart-understanding of the courage it takes to live daily with an observable difference.*"

> ~ **C. Joy Denny, BA, BRE**, Primary Specialist

"**Hi, I'm Me** *by Kelly Vurinaris is a wonderful book that reminds us all that being different is not only beautiful, but that we should embrace these differences in ourselves and others. We are all unique, whether it be in our appearances, personalities, talents, etc. Above all else, we need to be kind to each other and not only accept each other's differences, but also learn from them. If we all looked, acted, and did the same things, what a boring world that would be. The* message in this book, to be kind and accept one another as is, is a beautiful testament to the author's real life, where she instils this sentiment in her own daughter and everyone she meets."

~ **Heather Lean**, International Best-Selling Author of *Angel Grandma*

"**Hi, I'm Me** truly paves the way for ALL children. I love this book because it is so relatable even for myself as an adult. It shows the underlying beauty in the process of empowerment. It also shows the importance of positive introductions while sending the clear message that even when you are scared, taking a leap and discovering the outcome is rewarding. This is a thought-provoking book that promotes conversation about how important it is to be me, how important it is to be kind to others and ask those tough questions so that you can be better equipped to be an advocate for EVERYONE, including yourself."

~ **Roa Joli, ECE**, Director at Tiny Bees Childcare Montessori

"*What an awesome way to show courage and hope for a young child. I feel this book will be a great tool to help build confidence and self-esteem and overall self-acceptance.* **Hi, I'm Me** *is truly a must-have book!*"

~ **Dalandra Young**, #1 International Best-Selling Author of
Noonimals: First Day of School

"*Kelly Vurinaris has done such an extraordinary job explaining to children why people stare and what to do when they stare. I believe it will help parents and their children to understand how to communicate with others. She is brilliant with its simplicity. The book is beautifully illustrated. Well done!*"

~ **Timothia Sellers Hogan**, Best-Selling Author

"**Hi! I'm Me** is a wonderful book about building confidence, being true to oneself, and the honesty between a parent and child about the world around us. Author Kelly Vurinaris engages readers of all ages about the importance of being mindful and creates an environment of positivity even when a child's questions can be difficult to answer. This story is touching and a must for any home or school library. **Hi! I'm Me** is a reminder to be proud of who you are and the importance of thoughtfully educating others about our similarities and differences."

~ **Teresa Polito**, Educator

Hi, I'm Me

Written by Kelly Vurinaris

Hasmark
PUBLISHING
INTERNATIONAL

Published by
Hasmark Publishing International
www.hasmarkpublishing.com

Permission should be addressed in writing to Kelly Vurinaris at haykellyv@gmail.com

Editor: Allison Burney
allison.burney@gmail.com

Design: Anne Karklins
anne@hasmarkpublishing.com

ISBN 13: 978-1-989756-30-0
ISBN 10: 1989756301

*This book is dedicated to my amazing, smart, beautiful and
brave daughter who sees the best in everyone.
You never feel out of place and make every situation a positive one.
I cherish you and can't imagine my world without you in it.*

*You are my perfect angel, for now and forever.
Mommy loves you!*

Hi, I'm Chloe, and I see
people staring at me wherever I go.

Mom says that's because
they don't know me yet.

When I'm at
the playground and
someone is staring at me,

Mom says to say, "Hi, I'm Chloe."
Then they know me.

If they ask a question about my
tiny ears, that's okay because
they just want to know about me.

If I'm at soccer and my teammates
stare when I first meet them, I say,
"Hi, I'm Chloe."

If they ask me a question about my eyes,
I say I was born with big, blue eyes.
Now they know me.

When I go to Kindergarten, Mom says,
"Remember, everyone just wants to
know you." So I say,
"Hi, I'm Chloe. What's your name?"
Then they know me and stop staring.

They may ask about my hearing aid.

I tell them it's my

Superpower

that helps me hear better.

I may have a question for them, too.

When I'm in the library
and a bigger kid sees me and stares,
I sometimes get a little scared.

But as Mom always says,
they don't know me yet, so I say,
"Hi, I'm Chloe."
Now they know me and I feel better.

Mom says
everyone is different
in their own special way,
and that's what
makes us beautiful.

It's **okay**

to be me,

and no one
can be me but
me!

And I like that.

About the Author

Kelly Vurinaris is a mom, and like every mom, she wants the best for her child. Kelly created this book to help other children with differences understand that if you add your voice, you are no longer an object to be stared at; you're a person. This book is a true story taken from her own life. It represents what she has taught her daughter to do when someone is staring at her. Kelly is an advocate for kindness and acceptance for everyone and is committed to changing the world one face at a time.

Join Chloe at
www.confidentlychloe.com

HEARTS to be **HEARD**

Giving a Voice to Creativity!

With every donation, a voice will be given to
the creativity that lies within the hearts of
our children living with diverse challenges.

By making this difference, children that may
not have been given the opportunity to have their
Heart Heard will have the freedom to create
beautiful works of art and musical creations.

Donate by visiting

HeartstobeHeard.com

We thank you.

CPSIA information can be obtained
at www.ICGtesting.com
Printed in the USA
LVHW072011270921
698836LV00002BA/130